# THE GOLDEN GOOSE

## Margaret Hillert

### Illustrated by Monica Santa

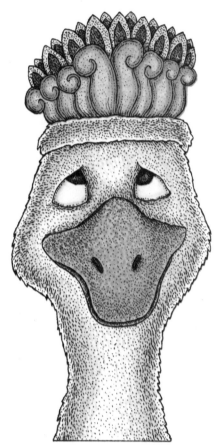

*f* FOLLETT PUBLISHING COMPANY/Chicago

Text copyright © 1978 by Margaret Hillert. Illustrations copyright © 1978 by Follett Publishing Company, a division of Follett Corporation. All rights reserved. No portion of this book may be used or reproduced in any manner whatsoever without written permission from the publisher except in the case of brief quotations embodied in critical reviews and articles. Manufactured in the United States of America.

International Standard Book Number: 0-695-40881-X Library edition
International Standard Book Number: 0-695-30881-5 Paper edition

Fourth Printing

You do not look happy, little one.
We want you to look happy.
What can we do for you?
Here is a ball to play with.

No, no.
I do not want it.
I do not want to play.

4

Oh, what can we do?
Who will help us?
Who can make you happy?

Something is in here.
Something little.
You will see.
Work and you will find it.

6

8

What is it?
What is here?
I will work and work.

Down, down it comes.
And look what is in here.
Oh, my.

I like you.
I want you to come with me.
Away we go.
Away, away, away.

Look, Mother.
Do you see what I see?
What is it?
Can you guess?

15

What do you have?
What is that?
We want to see it.

Oh, we can not get away.
Help, help.
We do not want to go with you.
We do not like this.

Look at this.
Here is work for me.
I have work to do.

20

Oh, Father, Father.
Come help us.
You are big.
You can help.

21

I will help you.
But what is this?
Oh, no!
Now I can not get away.

Go get it.
Go get it for me.
I like to play with you.

Oh, look at Mother.
Look at Father.
Run, run, run.

Come away, Mother.
Come away, Father.
Come here to me.
I want you.

I will help you.
I will. I will.

27

Oh, I can not do it.

Here we go.
Look at us go.
Up and up and up.

28

And here we come.

Down.
      Down.
            Down.
                  Down.
                        Down.

29

Look, Mother.
Look, Father.
Look and see.
Oh, that is funny.

30

It is funny.
It is. It is.
Now you look happy.
And we are happy, too.

31

# The Golden Goose

**Uses of This Book:** Reading for fun. This easy-to-read retelling of *The Golden Goose* is sure to excite the rich imaginations of children.

## Word List
All of the 57 words used in *The Golden Goose* are listed. Regular verb forms of words already on the list are not listed separately, but the endings are given in parentheses after the word. Numbers refer to the page on which each word first appears.

| | | | | | | | |
|---|---|---|---|---|---|---|---|
| **3** | you | | a | | see | **18** | get |
| | do | | ball | | work | | this |
| | not | | play | | and | **19** | at |
| | look | | with | | find | **21** | father |
| | happy | **4** | no | **10** | down | | are |
| | little | | I | | come(s) | | big |
| | one | | it | | my | **22** | but |
| | we | **5** | oh | **12** | like | | now |
| | want | | who | | me | **24** | run |
| | to | | will | | away | **28** | up |
| | what | | help | | go | **30** | funny |
| | can | | us | **15** | mother | **31** | too |
| | for | | make | | guess | | |
| | here | **6** | something | **16** | have | | |
| | is | | in | | that | | |